plaid castle Goat
publishing

Burrito Unicorn
Instruction Manual

CONGRATULATIONS!

on the exciting new addition to your family

Burrito Unicorns are filled with love and make incredible pets

BURRITO UNICORN
(Guerrero Unicornis)

Are they dinosaurs?
Are they alien in nature?
possibly both

This guide will give you
the important "do's and don'ts"
to caring for your burrite

Ancient markings on the
pyramids in Egypt and
historical sites in Mexico
depict the burrites

Fossils from these creatures
date them back to the Jurassic er.

The most modern discovery of these living beings came on March 7th 1988

Five full groups of these magnificient creatures were found

A team of anthropologists led by the infamous Theodore "Ted Tall Timbers" Furlonga spotted them on a lighthouse island off the coast of Oregon

The team studied these beasts for a little over three months before revealing to the world what they had discovered

The city of Cannon Beach
in Oregon commemorates
the discovery annually with
a big celebration

what is a burrito unicorn made of?

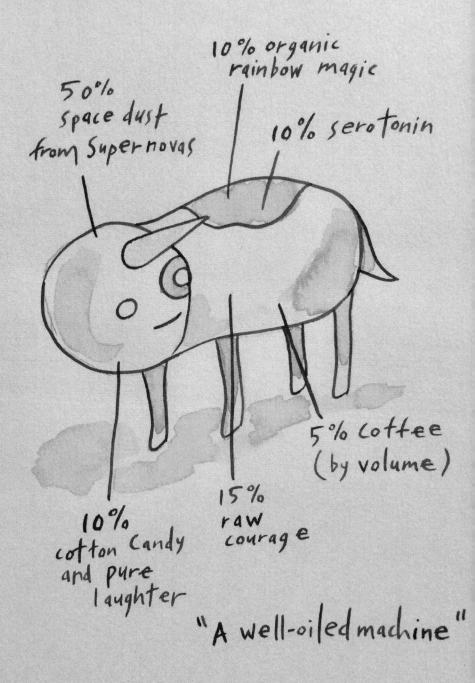

50% space dust from Supernovas

10% organic rainbow magic

10% serotonin

5% coffee (by volume)

15% raw courage

10% cotton candy and pure laughter

"A well-oiled machine"

In the wild
burrites run in groups
called "blessings"

They are very social
and like a group dynamic...

but in this animal
there are no alphas

they are all equal
and definitely individuals

when in a blessing expect to see some hardcore horseplay

The love to fly around together outside

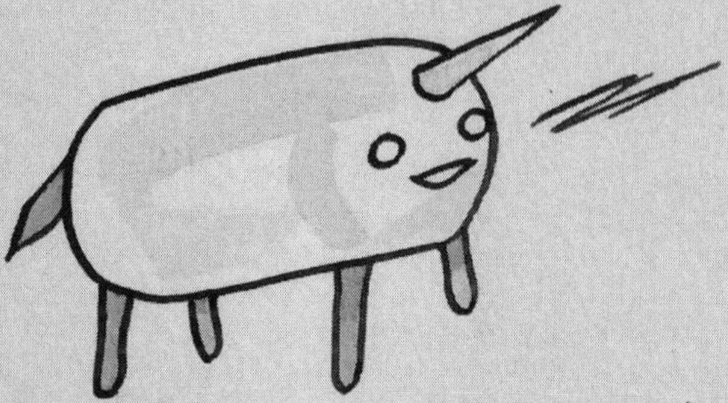

but remember

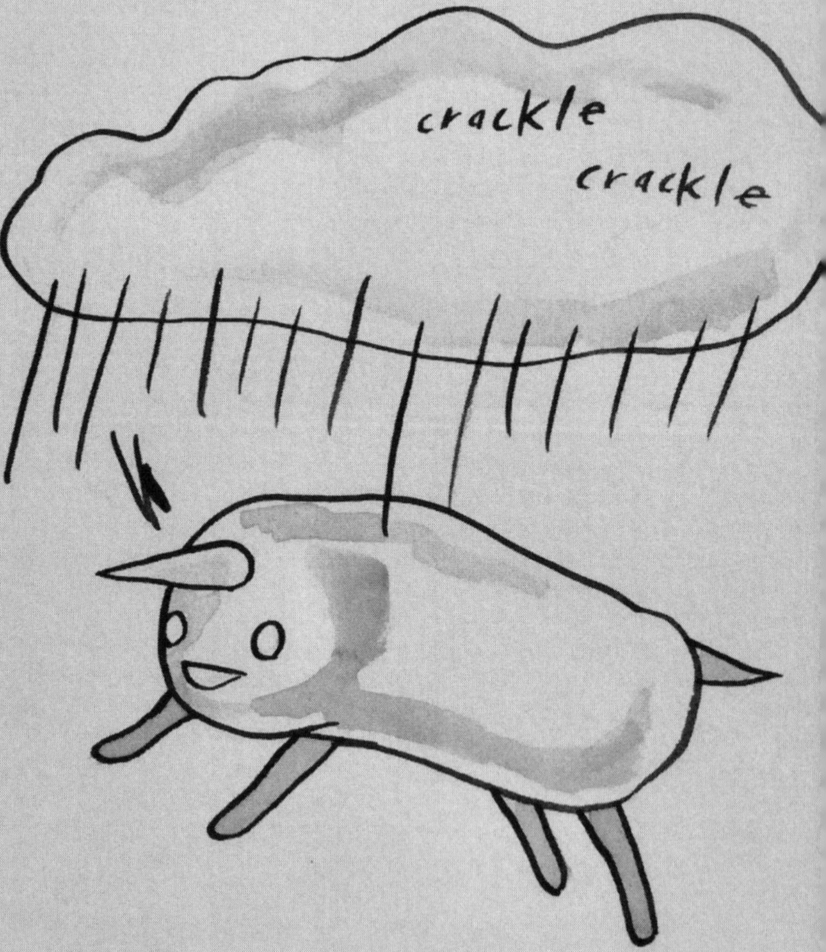

Burrito Unicorns are an incredible conduit for electricity
Keep them indoors during thunderstorms
ZAPPP!
AY|Y|Y|||Y|!!
one well placed lightning strike.. and..

... you got one crispy burrito

That crunchy shell is
very uncomfortable

It'll take about a month
for the hard shell to shed
and a new soft flour tortilla
to take it's place

Sugar free gum will keep your burrite's breath fresh and it's chompers clean as a whistle

These beasts are WAY too squirrely to hold down and brush those teeths

Also.. they love to blow bubbles
It's a win-win

Burrito Unicorns are very
sensitive to stress and they
pick up on unchecked anxiety

So be mindful of your anxiety
...relax
deep breath in
and exhale

be calm

No need to
"scoop the poop"

Don't even worry
about it

A burrito unicorn's feces
comes out in the form of a
cute super-clean mini rainbow

plink

it floats off into the sky

Burrito Unicorns live in
a gorgeous dream world
of extreme unconditional
love and pure hope

they are super optimistic
and are hopelessly attracted
to the positive

Keep that fire in them
alive and thriving

give them lots
of hugs

When a Burrito Unicorn
hits about two years of age

it loses it's magic
baby horn

it'll be stunned at first

it'll feel like it has
a "phantom limb" horn

put it in an Elizabethan Collar,
otherwise known as a Cone of Shame
for two weeks

that's how long it will take
for the spanking brand new
enchanted adult horn to grow

this horn is 100% more
fortified with magic
than the baby horn

... and even glows in the dark

when a burrito unicorn
gets super excited

it will lapse into a state
called "manic/giddy"
and will form bright
stars in it's eyes

these stars will shoot out
over and over until
the burrite calms down

The stars will
hover for a moment
then float off
into the sky

make sure that a window is
open or you'll end up with a
room full of stars

it can get real messy

don't let your burrite
roam free all morning
in the neighborhood

they love to knock over
trash cans and scarf down
the sick contents

Your neighbors will be pissed

...and to add a little bit
more to your headache

the disgusting trash that isn't
consumed will be happily rolled in
by your unicorn

YAY!!

whatever you do...

do not cut your
burrito unicorn
in HALF..

each side will form into a
complete, separate unicorn

this information was utilized and
put into action a little while back
when the burrito unicorns were
considered endangered

This is how they ended up on
the overabundant species list

when tucking your burrite
in at night

Keep the blankets loose

don't make the covers
all tight

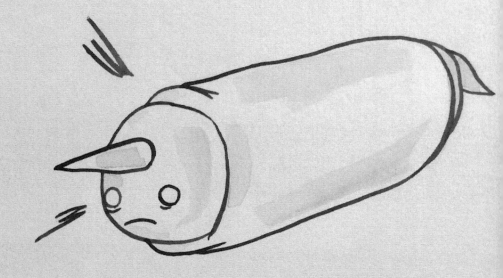

it is already a burrito..

it doesn't need any
extra tight wrapping

don't let your
burrito unicorn eat
"people food"

it has a very,
very fragile
digestive
system..

and should only be fed
jellybeans and fresh salad

a diarrhea rainbow might be breathtaking

.. but seeing a burrite in such distress...

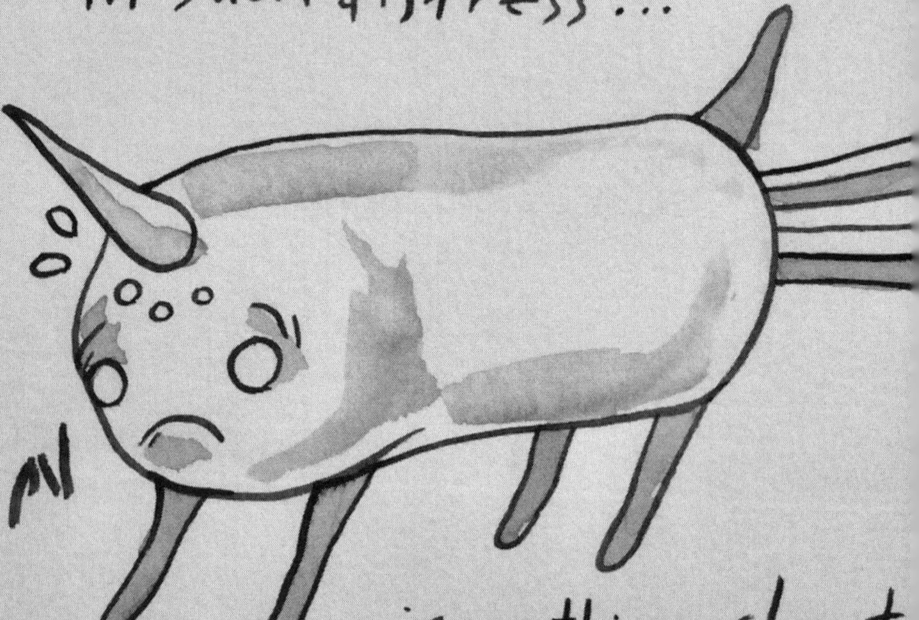

is nothing short of heartbreaking

Burrito Unicorns and spiders have had a complicated relationship for a long, long time

8 legs plus 8 eyes equals scary!!

your burrite's blood pressure
will go through the roof

Keep it away from the
creepy crawlies

like cats
Burrito Unicorns love to climb trees, then act like they're stuck up there

hold off on calling the fire department
as soon as it calms down a little, it'll remember that it can fly and come out of the tree

remember...

lots of hugs

Don't lie to your burrite

one lie will just lead
to another

be honest

it's easier that way

OH YEAH!!

They love coffee!

cheap coffee
expensive coffee
lattes
Americanos
Mochas
Whatever

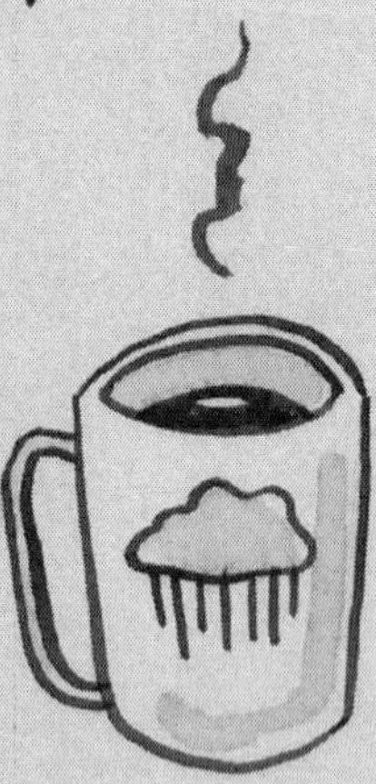

boing!

they want it
a lot of it

To keep your burrite's
mental state at 100% positive

pacify it in ice cold water
once a month

a river or the ocean
is ideal for this

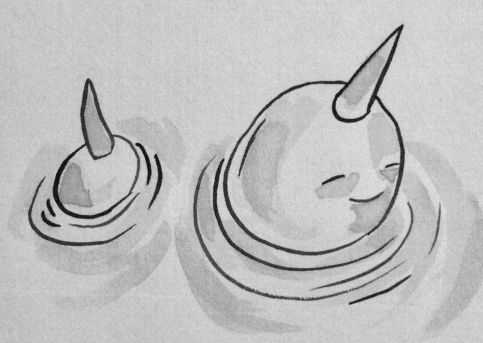

let your unicorn
become one with the tranquil
frigid water for about twenty
minutes

To keep your burrito unicorn fit

get it an exercise ball
the key to a burrite's ability
to fly is centered in their core

keep those abs tight

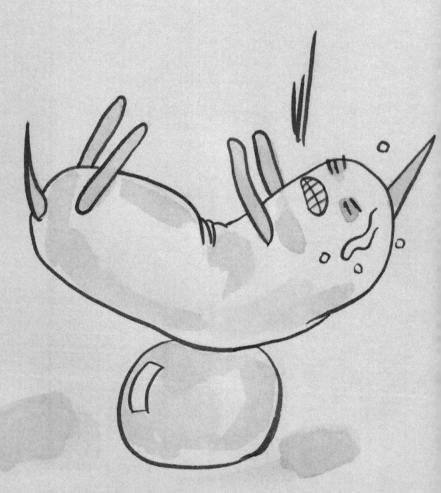

this is the best way to keep
it strong and able to fly freely

Burrito unicorns love
adventure and the unknown

they become very bored
with routine

This makes them very prone
to running away, don't take
it personally and don't worry

Your burrite will
wander back

cookie

...as soon as it
gets hungry enough

Keep your burrito unicorn happy

and it will keep you happy
good times!!

Yip!!

Get to know your burrito unicorns

Here are some burrites
that we've run into lately

Pablo

Pablo is prone to running away

He has intense wanderlust

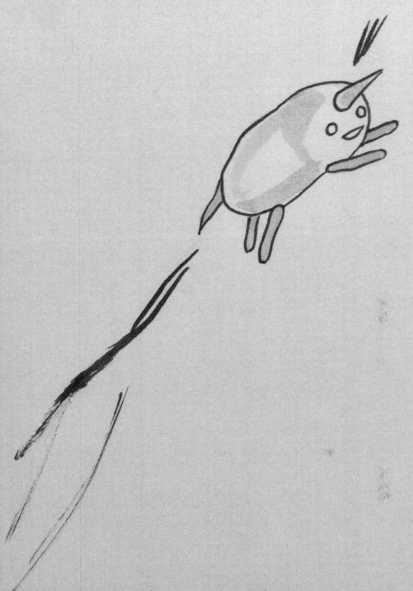

He is known to disappear
in pursuit of adventure...
at any moment's notice

Pablo's owners used to put out "lost" flyers

He's at the age now.. they know he's always coming back.. they know traveling makes him happy

cookie!

cookie is a tiny burrito unicorn
he has spots that make him
look like a chocolate chip cookie

Cookie feels most comfortable in the clouds

Turnip

Turnip is an introvert
she's a loner

Approach Turnip too quick
and you'll get flashed the teeth

she likes to be left alone

Bellingham

He is a broken horned
burrito unicorn

That doesn't hold him back at all,
he is very hyper and loving

Pico and Paco

These two smaller than average size twin burrito unicorns don't like to be separated

Ever since getting poked in the eye with a branch after rushing into some bushes...

Pico wears safety glasses at all times

The wild Burrito unicorns of Seahurst (the Seahurst 5)

This blessing of five is nocturnal and undomesticated, living in the forest just north of Burien, Washington

Beautifully haunting songs
have floated out of these woods
for years.. it's what tipped the
neighbors off to the burrites

The "Burien Birders" association
has named them

Juan-Antonio
(a tripod)

Paloma

che

Sante Fe

and Aurora

Scalvin

Scalvin was separated from his
blessing in New Zealand and spent
a year hiding in a cave, he wasn't
sheared for that entire year

Scalvin looks like a
small woolly mammoth...

without the tusks

Bunker

Bunker is sturdy
and very strong willed

He is impulsive...
a little rough around
the edges,

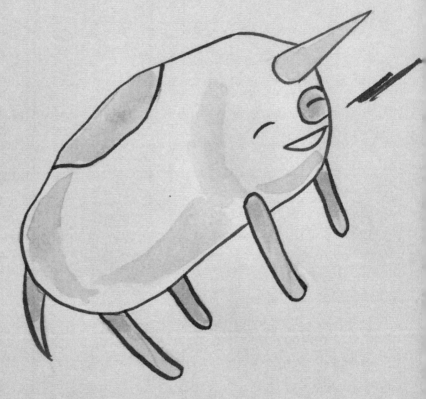

And he has a really
kind heart

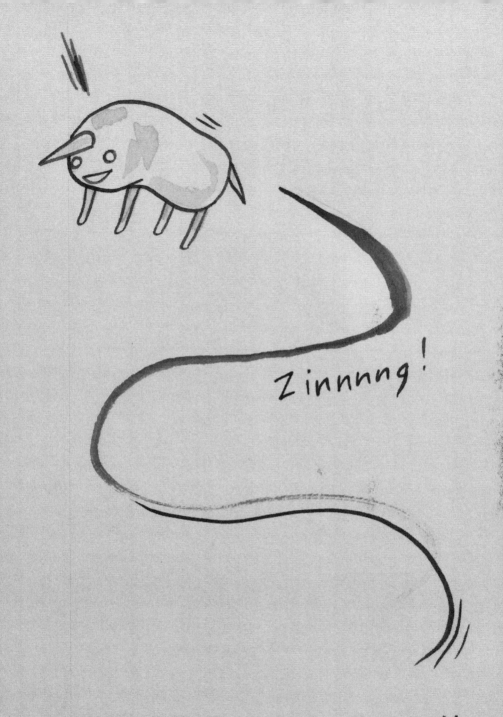

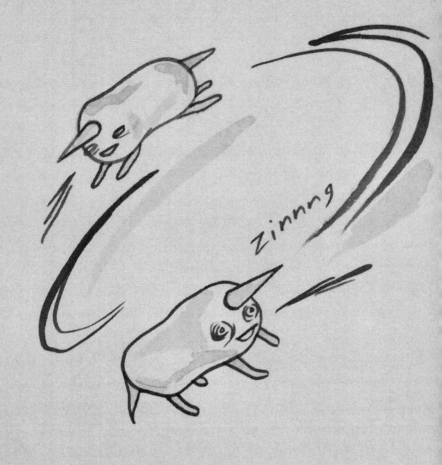

Dizzy gets moving so quick
that sometimes he opens
portals

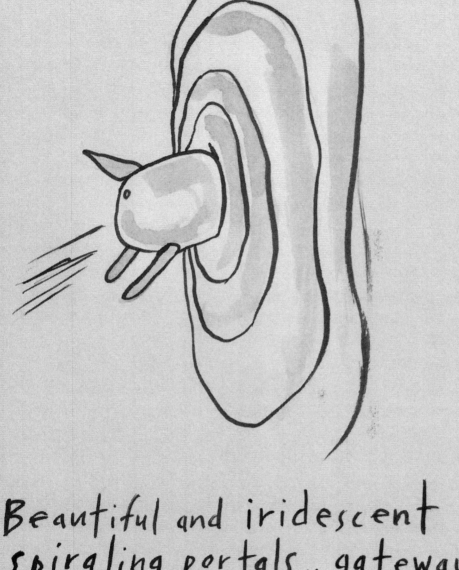

Beautiful and iridescent
spiraling portals.. gateways
to distant lands

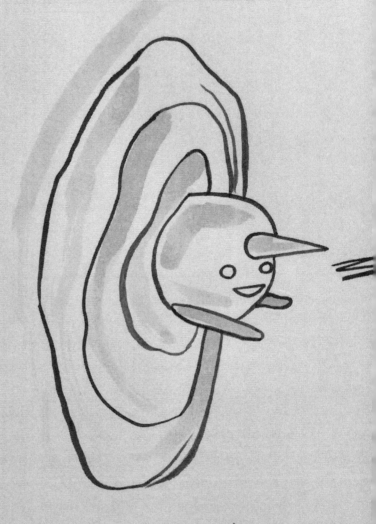

Dizzy has traveled through
multiple dimensions to all
the great destinations...
all over the earth

Adopt a Burrito Unicorn

These amazing creatures
will bring a lot of love
and warmth to your family

HAVE FUN TODAY !!

Starheadboy is a visual artist and writer from the beautiful Pacific Northwest

He spends most of his time drinking cheap beer, listening to podcasts, and hanging out with Crosby the boxer

He likes sunsets, taking the scenic route, and living out of his imagination

starheadboy.com

plaid
Castle goat

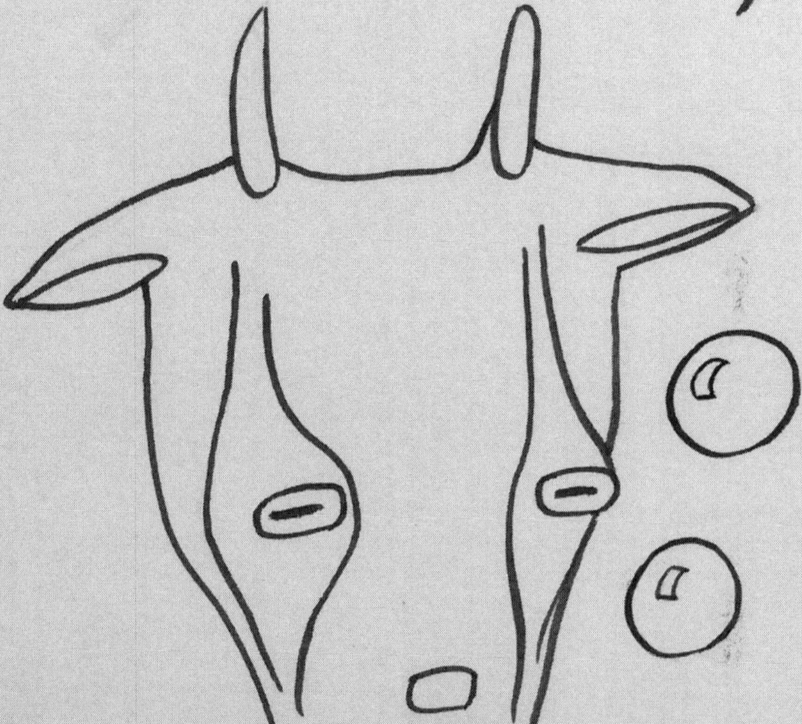

publishing

Made in the USA
Monee, IL
22 January 2023

24681064R00053